the bad wind and the 3 clouds

SRA/McGraw-Hill
Columbus, Ohio

Siegfried Engelmann
Elaine C. Bruner

www.sra4kids.com

Send all inquiries to:
SRA/McGraw-Hill
8787 Orion Place
Columbus, OH 43240-4027

Printed in the United States of America.

ISBN 0-02-686432-0

11 12 13 14 15 BSF 08 07 06 05

a mother cloud and father cloud said, "we will go out with our little cloud."

and they did. the 3 clouds went ōver hills and ōver lakes. every now and then the mother cloud tōld the little cloud, "look at this," or "look at that."

the 3 clouds did not plan to go far,
but a bad wind looked at them and said,
"I will blōw those clouds far awāy."

the bad wind came at the 3 clouds
like a shot.

"hō, hō," the wind said, "I will see
how far they go when I do my best
blōw."

again, the wind came at the clouds
and made the 3 clouds flȳ this wāy and
that wāy.

"help, help," the little cloud yelled.
"I am goin͡g far from my mom and
dad."

the mom and dad said, "we must stop that bad wind."

the two clouds let out a loud sound of thunder. that scāred the wind, but the wind did not stop. then the two clouds let out big shēēts of rāin. the wind still did not lēave.

the little cloud said, "I will help. I will make thunder, and I will make rāin."

the little cloud made a little thunder and a little rāin.

then all 3 clouds made thunder and made rāin at the same time.

boom went the thunder. down came the rāin. the bad wind was wet.

the wind stopped and said, "this
thunder is too loud fōr me and I hate
to get wet." so the wind left.

now the little cloud is back with his
mom and dad. the 3 clouds are happy
again.